COLOR YOUR OWN

THOR

Art by

**ALAN DAVIS, MARK FARMER,
JACK KIRBY, WALTER SIMONSON,
OLIVIER COIPEL, MARK MORALES,
JOHN ROMITA JR., KLAUS JANSON,
FRANK CHO, JOHN BUSCEMA, JOE QUESADA,
RUSSELL DAUTERMAN, VINCE COLLETTA,
JOHN VERPOORTEN, SAM GRAINGER,
STEVE EPTING, MIKE ESPOSITO, SAM ROSEN,
THONY SILAS, NELSON DeCASTRO,
TERRY PALLOT, DICK GIORDANO, BOB LAYTON,
RON FRENZ, BRETT BREEDING,
RONAN CLIQUET, AMILTON SANTOS,
CHRIS SAMNEE & MARK BROOKS**

Collection Editor: **Jennifer Grünwald**
Assistant Editor: **Caitlin O'Connell**
Associate Managing Editor: **Kateri Woody**
Editor, Special Projects: **Mark D. Beazley**
VP Production & Special Projects: **Jeff Youngquist**
SVP Print, Sales & Marketing: **David Gabriel**
Book Designer: **Adam Del Re**

Editor in Chief: **Axel Alonso**
Chief Creative Officer: **Joe Quesada**
President: **Dan Buckley**
Executive Producer: **Alan Fine**

Thor created by
Stan Lee, Larry Lieber & Jack Kirby

D1067102

OLIVIER & MORALES

-2009-